The Nostalgia Collection

Teddy Tail

Introduction by Mary Cadogan

The Nostalgia Collection: Teddy Tail

ISBN 0 948248 62 9

Published by HAWK BOOKS LIMITED
Suite 309, Canalot Studios, 222 Kensal Road, London W10 5BN.

This edition Copyright © 1990 Hawk Books Ltd.
Teddy Tail Copyright © 1990 Associated Newspapers.

Designed and Edited by Mike Higgs Graphics.

Printed in England.

'TEDDY TAIL OF THE DAILY MAIL'

by Mary Cadogan

Anthropomorphic animals have always hit a high note in British newspaper comic strips. Overflowing the "kiddies' corners" where they often kicked off, they seem to have appealed as strongly to adults as children. Although Teddy Tail was not the first furry newspaper cartoon hero, his predecessors (notably Tiger Tim & Co in the 1904 *Daily Mirror)* were more spasmodic in their early appearances. The *Daily Mail's* astoundingly resilient rodent achieved the distinction of starring in Britain's first *daily* strip. Launched on 5th April 1915, Teddy Tail of the Daily Mail became a byword; his career spanned forty-five years, while his popularity (and the battle for increased circulation) was to inspire the creation of other animal strip heroes, including Pip, Squeak and Wilfred in the *Daily Mirror,* Bobby Bear in the *Daily Herald* and Rubert Bear in the *Daily Express.*

With a short gap during the Second World War Teddy's colourful and engaging antics were to continue until 1960. His originator was Charles James Folkard — an artist then already well known for his illustrations of nursery literature and children's classics which deftly blended naturalism with elements of caricature. A man of many talents, he started out as a conjuror and later wrote several plays and pantomimes for children. Folkard stuck with the strip until the later nineteen-twenties, when his brother Harry took over.

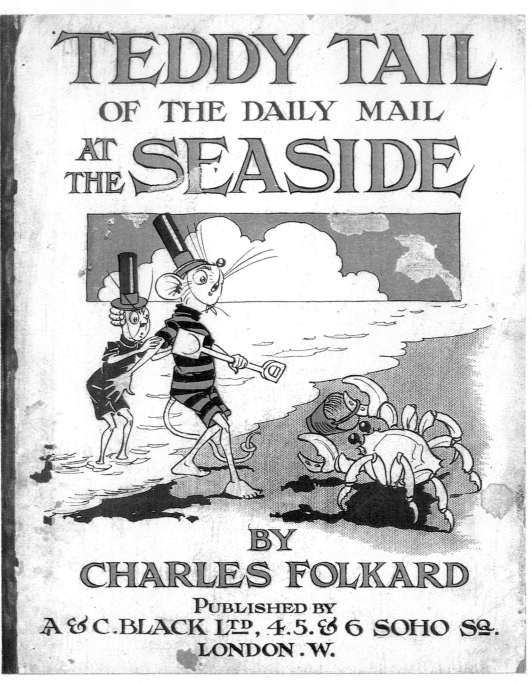

An early Teddy Tail book showing Charles Folkard's version of the mouse.

By the early 'thirties' the *Mail* had found a way for its magnificent mouse to pull in still more readers. A give-away comic starring him was issued with the paper from 8th April 1933. This large and lively *Boys and Girls Daily Mail* ran for four and a half years, appearing at various periods once, twice and even three times a week. Its popularity — and indeed Teddy Tail's nineteen-thirties' heyday — owed a great deal to the fact that from November 1933 Herbert Sydney Foxwell took over the strips. Foxwell had been drawing for the Amalgamated Press papers from 1913 in *My Favourite Comic, Comic Cuts* and *Puck* and had become celebrated for his splendidly bright and bold depiction of Tiger Tim and his assorted animal mates in *Rainbow, Tiger Tim's Tales, Tiger Tim's Weekly* and *Playbox*.

There was a flourishing Teddy Tail League which was featured prominently in the comic. Members proudly wore its red and black enamelled badge, acknowledged each other by making its secret sign, and were sent full colour Foxwell designed cards on their birthdays. Mousey merchandising spinoffs proliferated — from jigsaws and cut-outs to biscuits and books. The Teddy Tail Annual, appearing from 1934 to 1942 and then between 1949 and 1962, was a wonderfully satisfying enhancement of any child's Christmas. Foxwell's covers, endpapers and strips for it during the thirties are gems of illustrative exuberance. Sadly this gifted artist died of natural causes in 1943, while only in his early fifties. (He was on military service at Aldershot, and had been an army officer in both world wars). Teddy's exploits were temporarily halted by hostilities, but he bounced back into the *Mail* in

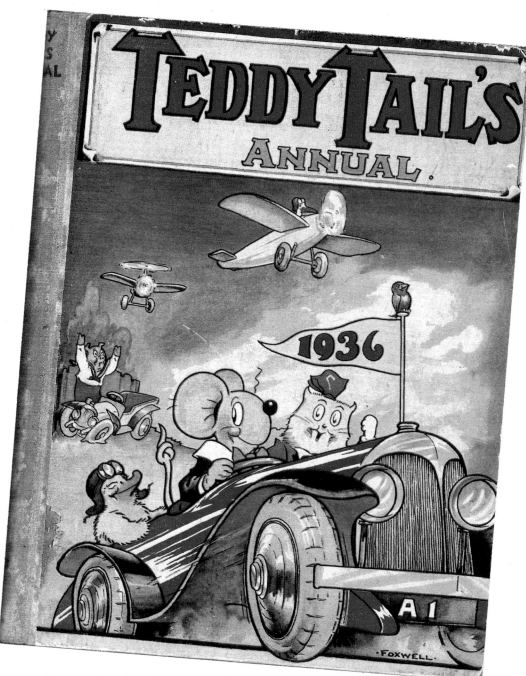

Herbert Foxwell's Teddy Tail from the cover of the 1936 annual.

1946, and was then drawn until the end of his run in the paper and annuals by Arthur Potts and W.T.J. Glenn.

His character development is fascinating. Folkard started him off as half-animal and half-human boy; no-one semed to find it strange that he soon became encased in Eton suits and collars (a garb then used throughout his career).

In Folkard's strips (which were reprinted in hard covers between 1915 and 1926) Teddy is skinny and slightly spikey. He engages in time shifts, trips to fairyland, other exotic locations and is often accompanied by the rather mysterious insect, Dr. Beetle. When Foxwell took over he rounded Teddy out and gave him a similar setting to that which had worked so well for Tiger Tim — a boarding-school with a teacher-cum-surrogate mother (in this case Mrs. Whiskers) in charge. He built up Teddy's friendships with his school-mates Kitty Puss, Piggy and Dougie, the baby duck. Cosiness became the keynote; the Whisker Pets were adventurous, but in the carefully controlled confines of home and nursery school — the familiar world of Teddy's most youthful fans. Foxwell made him mischievous but never malicious; he was also extremely competent, driving cars and piloting aeroplanes with panache, but most of all enjoying pranks and parties and lots of play (no-one seemed to study hard at Mrs. Whisker's school) in that timeless world of childhood in which we can still delight when we re-read Teddy Tail's engaging exploits.

Arthur Potts' version of Teddy Tail.

TEDDY TAIL'S ORCHESTRA BROADCASTS.

FOXWELL

Hallo, everybody!" cried Teddy Tail. "You are now listening to Teddy Tail and his Noisy Boys. We will play you the first selection from 'Song of the Farmyard.'" "Goodness!" exclaimed Mrs. Whisker, covering her ears. "If that's the first selection, I hope it is the last one too!" "Doodle-doo-hoo!" crooned Dusky Dick, strumming his home-made banjo. "We play all de day-ay in de new mown hay-ay." "Jolly good!" cried Piggy. "But—I've just remembered —I forgot to connect up the microphone! Good-night, everybody!"

A delightful illustration by Foxwell from the 1936 annual.

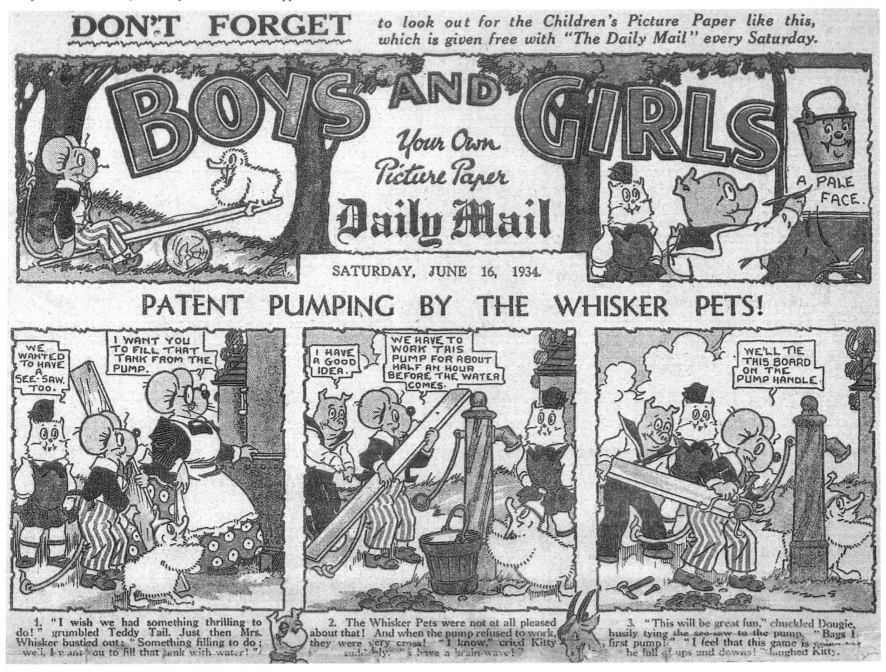

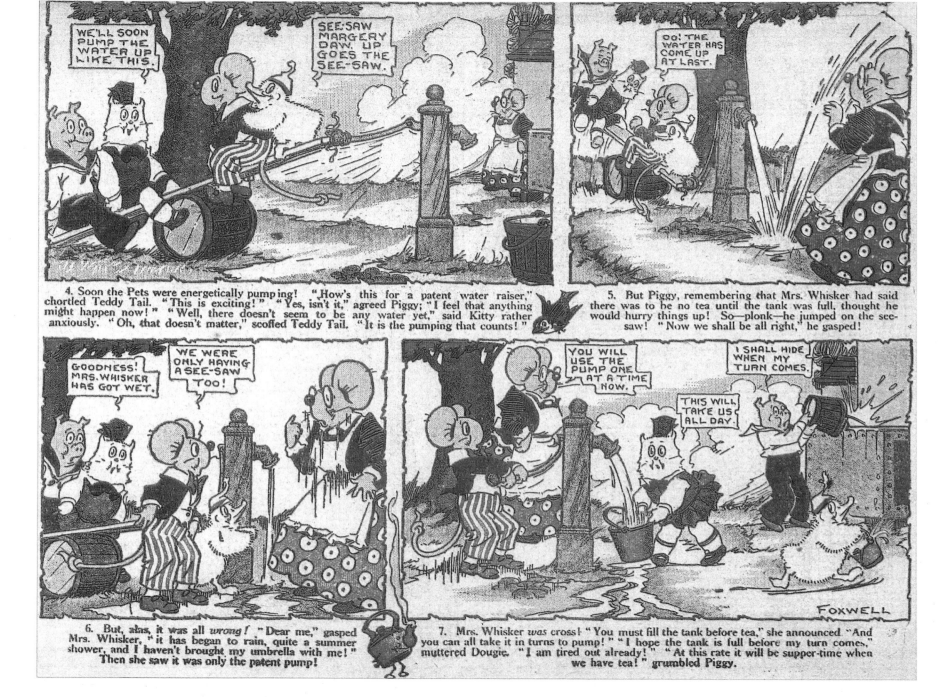

4. Soon the Pets were energetically pumping! "How's this for a patent water raiser," chortled Teddy Tail. "This is exciting!" "Yes, isn't it," agreed Piggy; "I feel that anything might happen now!" "Well, there doesn't seem to be any water yet," said Kitty rather anxiously. "Oh, that doesn't matter," scoffed Teddy Tail. "It is the pumping that counts!"

5. But Piggy, remembering that Mrs. Whisker had said there was to be no tea until the tank was full, thought he would hurry things up! So—plonk—he jumped on the see-saw! "Now we shall be all right," he gasped!

6. But, alas, it was all *wrong!* "Dear me," gasped Mrs. Whisker, "it has began to rain, quite a summer shower, and I haven't brought my umbrella with me!" Then she saw it was only the patent pump!

7. Mrs. Whisker *was* cross! "You must fill the tank before tea," she announced. "And you can all take it in turns to pump!" "I hope the tank is full before my turn comes," muttered Dougie. "I am tired out already!" "At this rate it will be supper-time when we have tea!" grumbled Piggy.

TEDDY TAIL'S PRESENTS COME BY AIR MAIL.

1 "I hope Santa Claus leaves me more than one engine this year," said greedy Piggy. "Well, Teddy replied, "We mustn't leave our stockings down here—Santa is coming by air tonight."

2 "Dear me," Santa Claus exclaimed, when he landed. Four stockings on the roof! I'll put something special in them." "Ssh!" whispered Kitty Puss.

3 When Santa had gone the Pets ran to their stockings. "Help!" gasped Teddy. "They're filled with snow!" groaned Dougie. "No choes—no toffee!" "And I'm a hungry Duck."

4 "Where have you been?" asked Mrs. Whisker. "I have a sack of toys for you—they were dropped from an aeroplane." "Hooray," cheered Teddy. "A merry Christmas."

TEDDY TAIL
DRESSES UP FOR CHRISTMAS!

Panel 1 speech: GO AND MAKE YOURSELVES COSTUMES TO WEAR FOR CHRISTMAS.

I AM GOING TO MAKE MINE IN A ROOM BY MYSELF.

SO AM I!

1. "How would you like to have a fancy dress party at Christmas?" said Mrs Whisker. "Fancy dress!" echoed Teddy Tail delightedly. "That will be lovely!" "Well, run along and make your costumes," beamed Mrs. Whisker. "You will find plenty of materials in the attic."

Panel 2 speech: THE OTHERS WILL NEVER THINK OF THIS COSTUME.

I SHALL LOOK NICE AS SANTA CLAUS.

"Let's each make our costume in secret," Teddy suggested. "Then we shall be able to surprise each other!" So each of them found some material and set to work. "I wonder if a beard will tickle," chuckled little Dougie. Behind the screen, Teddy was thinking the same.

Panel 3 speech: WELL! YOU HAVE BOTH THOUGHT OF THE SAME COSTUME.

SO WE HAVE!

3. Kitty Puss and Piggy were ready first. "Gracious!" gasped Mrs. Whisker, when she saw them. "You're both Santa Claus!" "So we are!" Piggy exclaimed from the depths of his beard. "Well, Kitty, I shouldn't have known you!" "I don't know myself!" Kitty giggled.

Panel 4 speech: HA! HA! HA! I WONDER WHAT THE REAL SANTA CLAUS WILL SAY?

MRS. WHISKER THINKS IT'S FUNNY, I DON'T.

4. When Teddy and Dougie came in they were dressed as Santa Claus too! "I must be seeing double!" Teddy gasped. "Triple," Dougie put in. "What about me?" "If you're all dressed as the same person," smiled Mrs. Whisker. "You'll only want one person's tea!" They soon settled that!

FOXWELL

'Teddy Tail and The Cavemen' — a comic strip adventure by 'Spot'

DOCTOR BEETLE'S BLUNDERBUSS ROARS OUT AS HE PULLS THE TRIGGER. THE CAVEMEN SCATTER AS THE BULLETS WHIZZ PAST THEM.

21

DOCTOR B'S BLUNDERBUSS SMOKES FURIOUSLY... THE CAVEMEN SCATTER IN ALL DIRECTIONS. THE POOR TROGLODOPUS IS MORE SCARED THAN EVER

22.

THAT SCARED 'EM AWAY!

QUICK! TAKE ME AWAY AND PUT ME INTO A ZOO FOR SAFETY! I'm TIRED OF ALL THIS!

THE TROGLODOPUS TRIES TO STEP ON BOARD THE "GOOD FRIEND" BUT NEARLY CAPSIZES IT. TEDDY, TOM AND DOCTOR BEETLE BEGIN TO WONDER WHAT TO DO.

39.

THE TROGLODOPUS ALMOST UPSETS THE BOAT, SO THE CHUMS DECIDE TO HITCH HIM TO THE BOWS IN ORDER TO SAIL BACK HOME.

40.

AND SO THE TROGLODOPUS SWIMS DOWN THE RIVER TOWING THE "GOOD FRIEND" WITH ALL THE CHUMS, ABOARD ON HIS WAY TO THE ZOO.

41

TEDDY FINALLY GETS HIS TROGLODOPUS TO THE ZOO WHERE THE POOR CREATURE SETTLES DOWN TO A HAPPY LIFE.

42

TO JOIN THE LEAGUE

THE Teddy Tail League is the jolliest imaginable, numbering as it does nearly three-quarters of a million members! Boys and girls in all parts of the world belong to the League, and what a cheery lot they are—you can tell them by the gaily-coloured enamel badges they wear!

All these hundreds of thousands of League Members have enrolled because they are the friends of Teddy Tail of the *Daily Mail*, and all Teddy's friends are friends of each other, so that when you join the League you will have friends in every corner of the globe.

Teddy Tail plans all sorts of jolly surprises for his friends, sends each a birthday card, arranges for special competitions and privileges, and is always pleased to answer any questions concerning their pets and hobbies.

Then, too, Teddy invites his friends to send him any snapshots they have taken, any verses or stories they have written, or any sketches they have made. For those which he is able to publish in the *Daily Mail*, he awards special prizes. The drawings which you see in the next pages are all the work of Teddy Tail League Members.

So if you would like to share in all the fun join now!

This is a very simple matter, as you will see when you read the directions which are to be found in the Boys, and Girls, section of the *Daily Mail*. You have to collect six Seals (one appears daily), and then exchange them for a jolly little enamel badge. When you have enrolled you are let into the secret of Teddy's sign—the sign which will make you friends with hundreds of boys and girls. Get the *Daily Mail* and read all about it!

COME AND JOIN US

.FOXWELL.

The Teddy Tail League was a popular club and this advertisement from the 1936 annual encourages more youngsters to join.